G000096801

Ancient Fables

Compiled by Wu Min

CHINA INTERCONTINENTAL PRESS

图书在版编目（CIP）数据

中国古代寓言故事：英文／伍民编；王国振，汉定，
吴晓芳译．—北京：五洲传播出版社，2010.1
（中国经典故事系列）
ISBN 978-7-5085-1771-1

Ⅰ.①中… Ⅱ.①伍…②王…③汉…④吴… Ⅲ.
①寓言-作品集-中国-英文 Ⅳ.①I277.4
中国版本图书馆CIP数据核字（2010）第009539号

出 版 人：荆孝敏
编　　者：伍　民
翻　　译：王国振 汉　定 吴晓芳
责任编辑：王　莉
设计指导：缪　惟
设计制作：袁　丹
插　　图：李思东

中国古代寓言故事

出版发行：五洲传播出版社
社　　址：北京市海淀区莲花池东路北小马厂6号
邮政编码：100038
发行电话：010-82001477
制版单位：北京锦绣圣艺文化发展有限公司
印　　刷：北京嘉彩印刷有限公司
开　　本：889×1194 1/32
印　　张：4.75
版　　次：2011年1月第1版 2012年1月第2次印刷
书　　号：ISBN 978-7-5085-1771-1
定　　价：53.00元

Preface

In Chinese, the word "yuyan" (fable) is composed of two words: "Yu" means implying something or expressing something in a disguised manner, while "Yan" means words or languages. Therefore "yuyan" means to explain a certain principle through the personification of invented stories or natural objects. This is the literal interpretation of the word "yuyan". In the daily life, the fable, a time-honored form of literature, often exists in long and large articles in the form of small stories to help explain the particular principle, or persuade individuals of the principle so that readers can understand the profound meanings of the articles.

Chuang Tze, a great philosopher in the Warring States Period (475 BC-221 BC) of China, first used the word "yuyan" in his articles. He wrote, "Most of the fables need to be read between the lines," which means that profound thoughts are expressed through simple stories. If further interpreted in the modern language, then Chuang Tze's statement can mean that the stories are used to express ideas of the authors—ideas that are hidden within the stories in which readers need to read between the lines.

In reality, fables are also a form of literature that matured a long time ago in both China and foreign countries. The well-known story—*The Farmer and the Snake*—is in fact a fable by a Greek called Aesop. In addition, *Bible* stories also contain many fable stories.

In general, fable stories are fictitious, that is, people invent them. True stories

often lack the overtones of fictitious ones, and therefore are very difficult to generate profound levels of wisdom. The power with which fables strike people is not whether they are true to reality, but rather the implied meaning that teaches people, advises people and enlightens people. Some fables have evolved into idioms. When we readily use these idioms, the wisdom of these fables will instantly spread into our intellectual space.

To this end, we have identified stories from the vast number of Chinese ancient fable stories, and compiled them into this collection. These fables are the finest and most famous in the Chinese history.

CONTENTS

水土不同·《晏子春秋》

Different Climates ◎*Yanzi's Spring and Autumn Annals*

Different Climates

◎Yanzi's Spring and Autumn Annals

Yanzi, a senior official of the State Qi in the Spring and Autumn Period (770 BC-476 BC), was to pay an official visit to the State Chu. Learning the news, King of Chu said to his ministers, "Yan Ying (formal name of Yanzi) is an eloquent person in the State Qi. Now he is coming to visit us. I am thinking of insulting him. Do you have any ideas?" A minister replied, "After he arrives here, we will tie up a person, and let him pass by Your Majesty. Then, you will ask, 'Where does this criminal come from?' We will answer, 'He is

a Qi native.' Then, you will ask again, 'What crime has he committed?' We will answer, 'He has committed the crime of theft.'"

After Yanzi reached the State Qi, King of Chu entertained him with a big banquet, and conferred him wines. While they were enjoying the delicacy, two soldiers escorted a tied-up strong man to King of Chu. Seeing the man, King of Chu asked in a high voice, "Who is this tied-up man?" The soldiers replied, "Your Majesty, he is Qi native, and committed the crime of theft." Hearing the reply, King of Chu turned to Yanzi with joy, "Do your Qi natives like stealing things since birth?"

Yanzi rose from his seat, walked to King of Chu with respect, and answered, "According to my best knowledge, orange trees will yield oranges if they grow to the south of the Huaihe River, but will yield bitter fruits if they grow to the north of the Huaihe River. Though the leaves of the trees are very similar, the fruits they yield are very different: one is sweet, and the other is bitter.

How come? This is because of the different climates. The tied-up person didn't steal anything when he was in the State Qi, but rather he learned to steal after he came to the State Chu. Isn't it because the climate in the State Qi makes the residents to learn to steal easier?"

Hearing the eloquent remarks, King of Chu was fully convinced, and smiled, "It is really inadvisable to make fun of a clever person. Today, I have failed to fool you, but had myself fooled."

In the Same Boat

◎*Sun Tzu*

As a result of the long-standing wars, the people of the State Wu and the State Yue were hostile to each other. They were not friendly at all when meeting the people from the other country.

One day, a person from the State Wu and another person from the State Yue happened to cross a big river in the same boat. They looked at each other not saying a word. When the boat arrived at the midstream, a wild wind crossed the boat all of a sudden. The boat shook wildly in the surging waves, and seemed to turn upside down immediately. At such a dangerous moment, the two persons left behind their hostility completely. They encouraged and helped each other, just like they were a pair of hands that depend on each other. They joined forces to stabilize the boat on the verge of capsizing, resisted the test by the storm, and finally reached the other bank safe and sound.

Talk Much or Little

◎ *Mu Tzu*

Ziqin, a student of Mu Tzu, asked his teacher, “Is it good to talk a lot? ”

Mu Tzu answered, “Toads and frogs shout aloud all day long until they become very thirsty. However, people are unwilling to hear them, because their sounds annoy people. However, roasters only crow at dawn every day, but attract much attention from all people. What is good about talking much? It is key to speak at the right moment.”

Ji Chang Learns Archery

◎ *Liezi*

Gan Ying was a great master of archery in ancient times. He could shoot animals and flying birds without missing the target. He had a student named Fei Wei, who performed even better than his teacher. Ji Chang wanted to learn archery from Fei Wei. The archery master told him, "You must learn not to wink before we discuss archery."

After returning home, Ji Chang laid under his wife's weaving machine, staring at the footplates up and down and trying not to wink. After practicing this for two years, he

would not wink even when his eye sockets felt like they were being stabbed with needles. He told his teacher what he had achieved, but his teacher said, "That is not enough, however. You must also develop good eyesight. The essence is that you must be able to see small things as big ones and dim thing very clearly, and then come to me again."

Following his teacher's advice, returning home, Ji Chang bundled a louse on the window with a hair drawn from a cattle tail. Facing southwards every day, Ji Chang stared at the louse. After ten days passed, the louse became to appear a little larger to his eyes. After three years, the tiny louse became as large as a wheel. When looking at other things larger than the louse, he saw them as huge as hills. Then, Ji Chang used a bow decorated with the cattle horn from the State Yan and an arrow made of the grass straw from the north to shoot at the louse. He did a wonderful job: the arrow impaled the center of the louse; while the cattle tail hair, used to suspend the louse didn't even break swaying on the window.

Ji Chang felt overjoyed about his progress, and told his teacher what had happened. Fei Wei jumped for joy, and said while patting Ji Chang on the shoulder, "You have mastered the skill of shooting."

Unnecessary Worry

◎ *Liezi*

There once lived a person in the State Qi in the Spring and Autumn Period (770 BC-476 BC). He was very anxious all day long, worrying about where he would escape to should the heaven fall and the earth collapse. With this concern, he didn't eat or sleep well, and thus became thinner and thinner as time went by.

Noticing this, one of his friends went to talk to him, "The heaven is nothing but thick air, which exists everywhere. In reality, you're living in heaven every day, your movement and even your breath can't live without air. You have been living in air for so many

years, and nothing has happened. Why should you worry about heaven falling?"

After hearing his friend's remarks, the person became even more worried, asking, "If heaven is composed of air, then how are the sun, the stars and the moon suspended? Will they fall and drop on us?"

His friend answered, "The sun, the moon and the stars are just air masses that can shine. Even if they fall, they will not cause death!"

The person was not convinced, further asking, "What will happen if the earth sinks?"

His friend consoled him, "The earth is just some soil that is piled up. Soil is omnipresent , and fills every corner firmly without a gap. Many generations have freely treaded on earth, but no accidents have ever happened. Why should you worry if it will sink?"

After hearing these remarks, the person was finally relieved, and gave up his unnecessary worries. His friend was pleased and smiled.

Refusing a Contemptuous Offer

◎ *The Book of Rites*

A grand famine hit the State Qi one year, and many people were starving to death.

A rich person called Qian Ao wanted to help the poor people, and put out some steamed breads and wine near the road, waiting for the hungry people to eat.

One day, a man looking like a beggar staggered slowly pass. The man was dizzy with hunger with his face covered with his sleeve, wearing a pair of very rugged sandals. Holding the food in the left hand and the wine in the right hand, Qian Ao shouted with an arrogant voice, “Hey! Come eat something!”

Hearing the contemptuous offer, the man removed the sleeve from his face, opened his eyes broad, and said to Qian Ao angrily, “No! Who cares about your bad things! I am starving like this because I refuse to accept the contemptuous offers along the way!” Upon hearing this, Qian Ao realized his prior voice was indeed insulting and felt hurt the dignity of the man, so he hurried to apologize. The man, however continued to refuse the food, but shortly fell to the ground because of hunger. He died soon thereafter.

偷鸡者 · 《孟子》

A Chicken Stealer ◎ *Mencius*

A Chicken Stealer

◎ *Mencius*

Once there was a person, who every day stole a chicken from his neighbor.

Someone advised him, "You're violating the code of conduct for an upright person. You had better give it up."

The person was reluctant to follow the advice. "Then, allow me to change my bad habit in phases," He said, "First, I plan to reduce the number of time I steal chickens to once a month. Then, I will stop stealing next year."

Since the person knew his actions were wrong, he should have stopped stealing immediately. Why wait for next year? If he postponed this, then he would lose the opportunity to correct his mistake.

以邻为壑 · 《孟子》

Pin on the Neighbor © *Mencius*

Pin on the Neighbor

◎ *Mencius*

Bai Gui was the prime minister of the State Wei in the Warring States Period (475 BC-221 BC).

One day, he told Mencius, "I am very famous for controlling floods, and stronger than Da Yu (a Chinese ancient hero who was famous for flood control)."

Mencius replied, "You're boasting. Da Yu controlled floods in line with the rule of water flow, and led floods into the ocean. In other words, Da Yu diverted floods into the oceans. However, you just raise the dams to make water flow into the neighboring states. Once water flows back, it will flood. Such flood control method is despised by the decent people. Your practice is really disgraceful!"

Climbing the Tree for Fish

◎ *Mencius*

In the Warring States Period (475 BC-221 BC), each state wanted to annex the other and become overlord. With its powerful strength, the State Qi was more ambitious. During his rein, King Xuan of Qi was eager to expand his territory by launching wars to build up his authority and become overlord.

Advocating a benevolent policy of no wars, Mencius paid a visit to King Xuan, and said, "I have heard that Your Majesty wanted to conquer the world through wars. This will absolutely not work. If you want the people

around the world to follow you, and realize your wish to unify the world, you must first rule your own state well so that officials, farmers, merchants and even tourists are willing to come and be a part of your territory where common people can live a happy life. If Your Majesty wants to conquer other states by force, it is just like climbing a tree to catch fish—you will exert effort but gain nothing, and never fulfill your original purpose. If you use such action to realize your wishes, then you will invite catastrophe."

King Xuan, however, turned a deaf ear to Mencius' advice, and attacked the other states. In the end, he did not realize his wish to unify the world.

Pao Ding Kills An Ox

◎ *Chuang Tze*

Pao Ding, a butcher, was ordered to kill an ox for King Hui of the State Liang. A sound would emit wherever he touched it with his hands, leaned on its shoulders, tread with its feet and support its knees. He sliced the ox very easily after inserting the knife, and the sound was pleasant to the ears. His movements were as beautiful as the Sang Lin dance in the Shang Dynasty, and the sound of cutting the meat was just as beautiful and moving as the Jing Shou music in the Yao era.

King Hui of Liang praised, “How have you developed such excellent skills?”

Putting down the knife, Pao Ding answered, “What I love is tao (meaning the rule in Chinese), which is even superior to this skill. When I became a butcher, what I saw was nothing but bulls. Three years later, what I saw was no longer just common bulls, but the gaps between their bones and the strike of tendons and vessels. Today, when I kill a bull, I don’t have to use my eyes, but just touch the bull with my heart and spirit, and its sensory organs and senses no longer function. I just kill the bulls with my hands through a mysterious intuition. I follow the natural physiological structure, and cut my knife on the gaps between bones to separate the meat from tendons and vessels naturally.

Blind Imitation

◎ *Chuang Tze*

There was a beauty called Xi Shi during the Spring and Autumn Period (770 BC-476 BC). She was so beautiful that each of her movements was regarded as perfect and worth imitation. However, she suffered great pain in her heart, and would press her heart with her right hand and frown. She was still considered beautiful even when doing this.

She had a neighbor, Dong Shi, who was very ugly. When hearing people say that Xi Shi looked very beautiful even when pressing her heart with the hand and frowning, Dong

Shi wanted to follow the suit. She too put her right hand on her heart and frowned. She walked to and fro the street, hoping people would say she was also very beautiful. To her surprise, people would shut their doors when seeing her act like this. Seeing this, one of her friends hurried to tell her in a low voice, "This is what Xi Shi is like when she is ill. She is very beautiful in doing this, but you won't be beautiful by doing the same."

Dong Shi only knew Xi Shi was very beautiful when frowning, but didn't know the reason. That is because Xi Shi was beautiful herself, and people all liked her. Beauty is not something that can be learned. Blind imitation will make the thing even worse.

A Frog in the Well

◎ *Chuang Tze*

Once there was a frog that lived in a well. One day, a giant turtle left his home in the East China Sea to play, and passed a well by chance. Looking up to see the giant turtle, the frog greeted him, "Hi, who are you? Where are you from?"

The giant turtle replied, "I am giant turtle, and come from the East China Sea. Why are you staying here? Come out right now. It's so crowded. Do you want me to help you out?"

The frog refused, "To tell you the truth,

I really don't want to go out. Here is so comfortable. It is like paradise. When I'm happy, I may jump on the edge of the well . When I feel tired, I may have a good rest in the cave on the wall of the well. When I am full, I may sing a few songs. When I have nothing to do, then I look up to see whether white clouds float past over the well. What a free life. The best place in the world is this well."

Hearing what the frog said, the giant turtle felt very funny, "But your well is really so small. Have you ever seen the ocean?"

The frog said, "Never. The ocean? Is it even greater than this well?"

The giant turtle answered, "The ocean is so vast that no one knows how vast it is, and it is so deep that no one can image its depth. When a flood happens on the land, the water in the ocean will not increase because of this, and when a draught hits the land, the water in the ocean will not reduce either. The ocean is boundless. I will fail if I spend my whole life

trying to find its end. The ocean is truly so enormous, so living in the vast ocean is true happiness!" The frog was very amazed at what the giant turtle said: There is such a large place as the ocean in the world. The frog realized that his vision was too narrow, and lowered his head.

鲁侯养鸟 · 《庄子》

Duke Lu Raises a Bird ◎ *Chuang Tze*

Duke Lu Raises a Bird

◎ *Chuang Tze*

Once upon a time, an ocean bird came to the suburb of the State Lu. To receive the bird, Duke Lu prepared a banquet in the ancestral temple. When the ocean bird appeared, Duke Lu ordered his men to play a musical composition called *Jiu Shao*, and tried to entertain it various kinds of meat. The ocean bird, however, was really frightened by such grand ceremony and became very depressed. The bird didn't even drink a cup of wine. It died three days later.

Duke Lu wanted to raise the bird in the way he was served, rather than the way a bird should be raised, so the result was not strange at all.

He's Jade

◎ *Han Feizi*

A man named He Shi in the State Chu discovered a rough jade in Chu Mountain, and submitted it to King Li with respect. The king ordered a jade craftsman to verify whether it was a true jade. The craftsman said, "It is a stone." Believing He was cheating, King Li order to cut down the left foot of He.

After King Li of the State Chu died, Wu became the king. He presented the rough jade to King Wu again. King Wu also let the jade craftsman to verify the rough jade, and the craftsman answered again, "It is a stone."

Also thinking He was deceiving him, King Wu cut down the right foot of He.

After King Wu passed away, Wen became the king. With the rough jade in his hands, He kept crying for three days at the foot of Chu Mountain. His tears dried, and finally blood shed out of his eyes.

Learning the news, King Wen sent a person to ask why he had kept crying, "Many people lose their feet as a penalty. Why are you so sad?"

He answered, "I'm not sad for the feet I' ve lost. I am depressed because the valuable jade is considered a stone. This is the true reason why I am so sad."

Then, King Wen immediately ordered the jade craftsman to refine the so-called stone, and actually got a valuable jade, and named it He's Jade.

远水不救近火 · 《韩非子》

Remote Water Saves No Near Fire © *Han Feizi*

Remote Water Saves No Near Fire

◎ *Han Feizi*

In order to maintain good relations with the State Jin and Chu, King Mu of the State Lu wanted to send the sons of some vassals to the two states. A minister called Chu suggested, "Let's say, for example, a child in the State Lu fell into water, you would send a person to the State Yue for help . Although people in the State Yue are good at swimming, the child will have already drowned when the Yue people arrive. Another example is that a fire breaks out and someone would go to the remote seaside to fetch water. No matter how

much water is fetched, he cannot save the fire. Water that is located in remote locations cannot save fires. Now, although the States Jin and Chu are very powerful, they are too far away from us. The State Qi is closest to us. However, you have not allied with it, but rather you have partnered with the States Jin and Chu. Then, if a disaster happens to the State Lu, who will save us in time?"

守株待兔 · 《韩非子》

Wait by a Stump for a Hare ◎ *Han Feizi*

Wait by a Stump for a Hare

◎ *Han Feizi*

Once there was a farmer in the State Song. He was weeding in the field on a very hot day, and his clothes got wet. Suddenly, he saw a hare running quickly. He ran after the hare, but the hare ran away like a shooting arrow. The hare, however, bumped against a stump in the field, broke its neck and died.

The farmer threw down his hoe and picked up the hare. He was overjoyed to capture a hare without any pains, and enjoyed

its good significance. He thought weeding was really a tiring job, and farming was also a tough job, but picking up hares without a struggle was much easier. So, he put down his hoe, and no longer worked in the field. Instead, he sat in the shade near the field all day long, dozing and waiting for more hares to collide into the stump.

After many days, the farmer did not get a single hare again. As he had also abandoned farming, his field was covered with weeds, which yielded nothing. All the people of the State Song laughed at him.

Self-contradiction

◎ *Han Feizi*

A person from the State Chu set up a booth at the marketplace to sell his spear and shield. The spear looked very sharp and the shield also seemed very solid. They attracted a large crowd.

The person boasted to the crowd, "My shield is so solid that nothing can penetrate it." Then, he started to boast about his spear, "My spear is so sharp that it can penetrate anything in the world."

Immediately, a voice came from the crowd, "It seems that your spear and shield

are both the best in the world. Then, how about using your spear to stab your shield to see what will happen?"

The person didn't know how to answer this question. The crowd burst into laughter and dispersed, leaving only the person with his so-called best spear and shield in the world.

画鬼最易·《韩非子》

Ghosts Are the Easiest to Draw © *Han Feizi*

Ghosts Are the Easiest to Draw

◎ *Han Feizi*

King of the State Qi asked an artist, who was drawing a picture for the king, "What is the most difficult thing to draw?"

The artist answered, "Dogs and horses are the most difficult things to draw."

King of the State Qi asked again, "Then, what is the easiest thing to draw?"

The artist replied, "Ghosts are the easiest to draw. People are familiar with dogs and horses, and see them every day so I can't draw them as I want. If my paintings fail to resemble them even slightly, people will notice it. However, things such as ghosts have never been seen so I can draw them as I wish, therefore they are the easiest to draw."

中州之蜗·《于陵子》

A Snail in Zhongzhou ◎ *Yulingzi*

A Snail in Zhongzhou

◎ *Yulingzi*

Once there was a snail in Zhoangzhou, who blamed himself for being incompetent. To counter this terrible notion of himself, he ambitiously decided to climb Mount Tai, but he knew he would need to take more than 3,000 years to reach the mountain top. He also wanted to view the Yangtze River and the Hanshui River in the south, but it also would need over 3,000 years of travel. Then, he calculated his life—he would only live for a few days. How could he realize such a great ambition in such a short period of time? Realizing this, he became so depressed, and died at a straw.

The mole cricket and the ant both laughed at the snail that aspired too greatly.

Birds of a Feather Flock Together

◎ *Lu's Spring and Autumn*

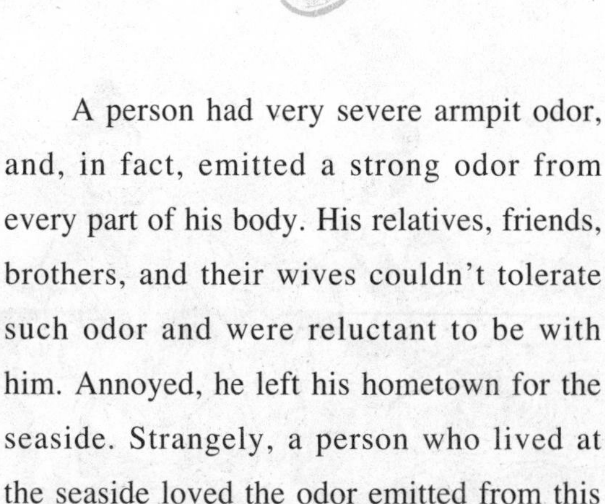

A person had very severe armpit odor, and, in fact, emitted a strong odor from every part of his body. His relatives, friends, brothers, and their wives couldn't tolerate such odor and were reluctant to be with him. Annoyed, he left his hometown for the seaside. Strangely, a person who lived at the seaside loved the odor emitted from this person, and of the followed the heels of this person day and night, smelling the odor with greediness. This story vividly tells the truth that " birds of a feather flock together. "

投婴于江·《吕氏春秋》

Throw a Baby Into the River ◎ *Lu's Spring and Autumn*

Throw a Baby Into the River

◎ *Lu's Spring and Autumn*

When passing by a riverside, a person saw a man who was about to throw a baby into the river with surging waves. The baby was so frightened and cried loudly. Another person came up to ask, "This baby is so young. Why do you want to throw him into the river?" The first person answered, "His father must be very good at swimming."

The person blamed, "Yes, his father is good at swimming, but is this baby also good at swimming? Your conduct will cause a tragedy!"

Marking the Boat to Look for a Sword

◎ *Lu's Spring and Autumn*

A person from the State Chu wanted to cross a river of enormous breadth that had surging waves. So, he boarded a small boat and asked the boatman to take him to the other side of the river.

The boat ploughed into the waves sailing forward while the person stood at the front of the boat, enjoying the beautiful views along the river. Suddenly, a wave came at the boat, and the boat bounced. Unable to stand, the person wobbled, and his sword fell into the water. He bent down in a hurry to mark the

shipboard from where his sword fell into the water. "This is where my sword has fallen into the water!" he murmured.

The boat finally arrived at the other bank. As soon as the boat pulled in, he immediately jumped into the water from the shipboard that he marked to look for his sword in the water.

The person spent more than half a day looking for his sword in the water, but in vain. He then had to come ashore in great disappointment.

He didn't realize that the boat had left the place where the sword had fallen into the water, but the sword was not moving along with the boat. How would he find the sword from the mark? Was it not very foolish to look for the sword like this?

Plugging His Ears While Stealing a Bell

◎ *Lu's Spring and Autumn*

Once upon a time, a person saw a beautiful bell suspended outside the gate of his neighbor's house, and wanted to steal it. One day, he discovered an opportunity when he saw his neighbor's gate closed. Looking around, he emboldened himself to reach the bell.

However, he suddenly realized that the bell would ring if he touched it, and he would be found out. That would be very terrible! So he came up with an idea, "If I plug my ears, won't I hear the bell ring?" Then, he found something to plug his ears, and stretched out his hand toward the bell.

Just when he touched the bell, it started to ring. Hearing the chime, the neighbor ran out to see the man stealing his bell, and caught him red handed.

However, the person was confused, "I plugged my ears, but how could you hear the bell ring?" Hearing his comment, his neighbor burst into laughter: This person was just deceiving himself, and trying to disguise something that could not be disguised. Isn't he troubling himself?

两虎相斗 · 《战国策》

Two Tigers Fight © *Strategies of the Warring States*

Two Tigers Fight

◎ *Strategies of the Warring States*

Seeing two tigers fight each other to eat the same person, Guan Zhuangzi wanted to kill them both. Guan told the person preventing him, "Tigers are very fierce beasts, and humans are nothing but a good meal to them. Now, two tigers are furiously fighting to eat the same person. Finally, the smaller tiger will be bitten to death, while the larger tiger will also be seriously wounded. After their fight, what I need to do is just to kill the wounded tiger. This is really something that kills two birds with one stone. I won't have to spend the strength of killing even one tiger, but earn the fame of killing two tigers. Why not?"

Bian Que Visites King of Qin

◎ *Strategies of the Warring States*

Bian Que, a famous doctor, paid a visit to King Wu of the State Qin. The king told Bian Que about his disease, and Bian Que requested an opportunity to cure the king.

However, the ministers of King Wu said, "The disease of the king is in the front of the ears and below the eyes. A cure may not necessarily help, but merely cause a negative effect that makes the ears deaf and the eyes blind."

King Wu told Bian Que about this.

Hearing the comments of the ministers,

Bian Que was irritated, threw away the stone needle, and said to King Wu, "You should have discussed the treatment with the people who know medicine. If you discuss it with those who have no knowledge about medicine, you will ruin yourself. If you govern the State Qin in this way, the State Qin will soon perish."

A Frightened Bird

◎ Strategies of the Warring States

Geng Lei, an archery master of the State Wei, stood on a high platform together with King of Wei, looking up to see flying birds in the sky.

Geng Lei said to King of Wei, "I can shoot down a bird, as long as I pull the cord without using an arrow."

King of Wei felt confused, "Have you developed your toxophilite skill to such an amazing extent?"

Geng Lei answered with confidence, "Surely."

After a while, a wild goose flew from the east. Geng Lei pulled the bow cord with force, and the wild goose indeed fell to the ground after the sound produced by the bow cord.

King of Wei was amazed, "Why have you developed your toxophilite skill to such an amazing extent?"

Geng Lei explained, "This is a wounded wild goose."

King of Wei asked, "How do you know this?"

Geng Lei replied, "This wild goose flew slowly, and cried sadly. It flew slowly, because it ailed from the original wound; and it cried sadly, because it has been away from the wild goose flock for a long time. Just because its original wound had not been cured, and its fear had not been removed, then the wild goose would think somebody wanted to shoot at it again when hearing the sound emitted by the bow cord. To escape, he wanted to fly high, but eventually it fell to the ground, because its original wound broke again."

A Fox in the Lion's Skin

◎ *Strategies of the Warring States*

The tiger hunts all types of animals to serve himself. One day, the tiger caught a fox.

Not afraid of the claws of the tiger, the fox said to the tiger, "How dare you eat me? The Lord of Heaven has dispatched me to be the king of all animals. Now, if you eat me, you will violate the command of the Lord of Heaven. You don't believe me? Then, I will let you see my power. You just follow me to see whether those animals will escape when they see me?"

Thinking the fox's remarks were

reasonable, the tiger walked toward the fox. Indeed, the animals all scattered upon seeing them.

The tiger didn't know the animals had escaped because they were afraid of himself, but thought they were really afraid of the fox.

The Snipe and the Clam

◎ *Strategies of the Warring States*

A snipe flew to peck the meat of a clam, just when the clam opened its shell to bathe in the sun. The clam forcefully closed the shell and pinched the snipe by the mouth.

The snipe said, "If it doesn't rain today and tomorrow, there will be a dead clam."

The clam didn't want to compromise, "If I don't let you go today and tomorrow, there will be a dead snipe."

The clam and the snipe both refused to give in. Soon, a fisherman appeared, and caught them both.

A Blessing in Disguise

◎ *Huainanzi* by Liu An

Once there was an old man, called Sai Weng, who lived near the border.

One day, one of Sai Weng's horses ran out of the border, and his neighbors all came to console him. Sai Weng, however, was not anxious at all, saying, "This is really no big deal. How do we know that losing a horse isn't actually a blessing?"

A few days later, the horse that ran out of the border suddenly came back, followed by a good horse from Hun ethnic tribe. This time, his neighbors all came to congratulate

him. However, Sai Weng was still as cool as a cucumber, "Thank you for your kindness. But the problem is: how do we not know that this isn't necessarily a bad thing?"

Sai Weng raised many good horses, and his son liked riding horses very much. One day, his son fell from the back of a horse, and broke his legs while riding it. His neighbors again came to console him. Sai Weng, however, said, "Thank you for your kindness. My son broke his legs, but why isn't it a blessing?"

One year later, the young people were all recruited to resist the furious invasion of the Huns. In the end, most of the young people died in the war, and only one out of ten survived. Sai Weng's son was not ordered to join the army because of his broken legs, and thus saved his own life and that of his father.

A fortune may change into a disaster, and a disaster may also change into a fortune. The principle behind this is very profound.

危如累卵 · 刘向《说苑》

As Dangerous as Stacked Eggs © *Shuo Yuan* by Liu Xiang

As Dangerous as Stacked Eggs

◎ *Shuo Yuan* by Liu Xiang

King Ling of the State Jin wanted to build a nine-story tower with a lot of money, and told his ministers, "If anyone dares to prevent me, I will kill him."

Hearing the news, Xun Xi, a minister of the State Jin, asked to have a meeting with King Ling. The king ordered his guards to pull the bow cords and pull out the swords, and received Xun Xi in such a frightening atmosphere.

Xun Xi said to the king, "I don't dare to prevent Your Majesty from building the tall tower. I am just having fun with Your Majesty.

I can pile nine chessmen and then put nine eggs on the chessmen."

Hearing this guarantee, King Ling smiled, "Now, you will have to show me."

Xun Xi calmed himself down, and displayed the game for the king with all his heart. He piled up twelve chessmen carefully, and put nine eggs one after another on the chessmen. This game was really exciting, and the guards all held their breaths. King Ling also felt very nervous and kept saying, "Dangerous! Dangerous!"

Xun Xi, however, said, "This is not dangerous, but there is something more dangerous than this!"

King Ling immediately asked, "Really? I would like to see what that could be."

Xun Xi answered, "If Your Majesty builds the nine-story tower, and then it will take three years and require a lot of residents to work on this project. As a result, men will not be able to work on the farm, the women will not be able to weave cloth, and money in the state will be used up. That is really dangerous!"

Mantis Stalks a Cicada

◎ *Shuo Yuan* by Liu Xiang

A cicada is chirping loudly in a tree in the garden, drinking dew and feeling very happy. However, the cicada doesn't know a mantis is stalking behind him. The mantis is bending its body and lifting its front claws to catch the cicada, but doesn't realize a yellowbird is approaching it. The yellowbird is stretching out its neck to eat the mantis, but doesn't think a person has already pulled out a catapult aiming at it.

The cicada, the mantis and the yellowbird are all thinking of the interest before their eyes, but don't see that danger behind them is approaching.

叶公好龙・刘向 《新序》

Lord Ye Loves Dragons © *New Preface* by Liu Xiang

Lord Ye Loves Dragons

◎ *New Preface* by Liu Xiang

Lord Ye loved dragons very much. His clothes hooks are painted with dragons, his wine set was also decorated with dragons, and the image of dragons was ubiquitous in his everyday life. It can be said that he lived among a group of dragon pictures. Learning Lord Ye loved dragons so much, the true dragon in the heaven was very glad, and left the heaven to pay a visit to Lord Ye. The dragon looked inside through the window of Lord Ye, and left its tail in the sitting room. Seeing the true dragon had come from the heaven and stayed at his home, Lord Ye was scared out his wits, lost the color in his face, cried loudly, and turned around to escape his home wildly.

In fact, Lord Ye didn't really like true dragons, but liked those things that looked like dragons. When he faced the true dragon, he had no choice but run away.

鸡犬升天 · 王充《论衡》

All Dogs Go to Heaven © *Lun Heng* by Wang Chong

All Dogs Go to Heaven

◎ *Lun Heng* by Wang Chong

To learn Taoism, Liu An, King of Huainan, invited people who know Tao, and preferred to give up the noble position as a king. Therefore, those worldwide experts in Tao assembled in Huainan, and the peculiar theurgy was all contributed.

Eventually, King of Huainan became an immortal as guided by the masters, and his family members and even the dogs and chickens became the immortals and went to the heaven. As a result, the dogs barked in the heaven and the chickens crowed in the clouds. This story shows that if a person succeeds, other people related to him will benefit.

一叶障目・邯郸淳《笑林》

Cover the Eyes With a Leaf ◎ *Jest Book* by Handan Chun

Cover the Eyes With a Leaf

◎ *Jest Book* by Handan Chun

There was once a person in the State Chu who was very poor and liked reading.

One day, when reading a book called Huainanzi, he found a line, "If somebody gets the leaf that a mantis uses to disguise itself when catching a cicada, he will be able to conceal his own body."

From the day on, he wandered the forest all day long looking for a leaf that a mantis uses to disguise itself when catching a cicada. Finally, he saw a mantis concealing itself behind a leaf before catching a cicada. He was overjoyed and rushed to pick the leaf. However, he dropped the leaf on the ground out of carelessness, and the leaf got mixed in with a lot of leaves on the ground. Unable to distinguish which leaf had just fallen, he had to fetch a few baskets of the leaves and take them home.

After returning home, he used one leaf after another to cover his eyes, and asked his wife, “Can you see me?” “Yes”, answered his wife. “Can you see me?” he picked up another leaf. “Yes”, answered his wife. Annoyed by his frequent question, his wife cheated him, “No, I can’t see you now.”

Happy to hear that, the person went to the marketplace with the leaf. He covered his eyes with the leaf, took the belongings of others and turned around to leave.

As a result, he was caught by a small official on the scene, tied and taken to the local government. The county magistrate accepted the case. After hearing the person tell the whole story about his stealing, the county magistrate didn’t punish him, and instead let him go.

Rubber Stamp ◎ *Jest Book* by Handan Chun

Rubber Stamp

◎ *Jest Book* by Handan Chun

Cui Lie, a senior official in the Han Dynasty (206 BC-220 AD), favored Bao Jian, a person living in Shangdang Region, and wanted to recruit him.

Hearing the news, Bao Jian wanted to visit Cui Lie very much, but worried that he would become a joke because of his very limited knowledge about etiquette. So he consulted with the persons who had visited Cui Lie about the details of etiquette. Someone told him, "When you visit Cui Lie, you will only have to follow the emcee, no

matter what he says." Bao Jian bore this in mind.

When meeting with Cui Lie, Bao Jian followed the emcee. When the emcee said, "It is time to kneel down."

Bao Jian immediately followed, "It is time to kneel down."

The emcee said, "Please take a seat, every gentleman."

Bao Jian followed the emcee immediately, "Please take a seat, every gentleman." Then, Bao Jian put on his shoes, and sat down.

When leaving the seat after the meeting, Bao Jian didn't remember where he had left his shoes because of anxiety.

The emcee told him, "Your shoes are on your feet."

Bao Jian closely repeated, "Your shoes are on your feet."

This story indicates that if a person just parrots others, then he won't have his own ideas.

折箭·魏收《魏书》

Break Arrows © *Book of Wei* by Wei Shou

Break Arrows

◎ *Book of Wei* by Wei Shou

Achai, the leader of the Tuyuhun Tribe, had twenty sons in all. One day, Achai told them, "Each of you must now go get an arrow, and put it on the ground."

After a short while, Achai called his brother Mu Liyan to come, and stated, "Now, pick up an arrow and break it." Mu Liyan broke the arrow very easily.

Achai said to Mu Liyan again, "Now, pick up nineteen arrows and break them."

Mu Liyan picked up nineteen arrows, but failed to break them, tired with a flushing face

and breaking into a sweat.

Next, Achai turned to his sons, "You have all seen that a single arrow is very easy to break, but many arrows bundled together are very difficult to break. Only if you join forces, can our country be consolidated and undefeatable."

Playing Music for the Cow

◎ *Collection of Hongming*

Long ago, there was a musician called Gong Mingyi who played the piano very well, and many people wanted to hear his performance.

One day, he played the piano in an open field. It was just the late spring with very beautiful views. In a good mood, Gong Mingyi played the piano better than usual, as the music was extremely pleasing to ears.

Seeing a cow eat grass in the grassland, Gong Mingyi suddenly wanted to play music for the cow. So, he started playing the piano to the cow.

Though he spared no effort and played the elegant music called Qing Jiao, the cow didn't react to his music at all, but instead kept eating grass.

Realizing the cow could not enjoy such profound music, Gong Mingyi changed to another composition. The music at times sounded like the sounds of a mosquito, a gadfly and a calf. Then, the cow shook his tail, and for some time, cocked its ears, and listened to the music wholeheartedly.

This story is used to ridicule the behavior of telling the profound rules to stupid persons, and also laugh at those who do not acknowledge the listeners when speaking.

后羿射箭・苻朗《苻子》

Hou Yi Shoots ◎ *Fu Zi* by Fu Lang

Hou Yi Shoots

◎ *Fu Zi* by Fu Lang

King of the State Xia ordered his men to set up a small target with an even smaller bull's eye. He said to Hou Yi, "Now, you will shoot the bull's eye. If you shoot it, I will bestow you a lot of money, and if you miss the target, I will deprive you of a lot of your feud." Hearing the order, Hou Yi became very nervous. His chest fluctuated and his breathing became very restless. Hou Yi started to shoot at the target. He missed the target with the first arrow, and missed the target again with the second arrow.

King of the State Xia asked Mi Ren, an official that educated in the royalty, "Hou Yi has never missed the target in the past. But this time, he missed the target twice. Why?"

Mi Ren answered, "During the shooting just now, the mood of joy and horror ruined him, and the prospect of the award money has become the disaster. If everybody can throw away the psychological burden of joy and horror, and leave the heavy bestowment behind, everybody in the world will become great marksmen."

One Thousand Coins Around My Waist

◎ *Collection of Liu Hedong*
by Liu Zongyuan

People in Yongzhou were all good at swimming. One day, a flood happened to the Xiang River, and a few people crossed the river in a small boat. When the small boat arrived at the center of the river, the boat broke, and all the people on the boat jumped into the river and struggled to swim towards the riverbank. One person swam very slowly, though he spared no effort.

His companion asked him, "You are the best swimmer. But how are you swimming so slowly?"

The person answered out of breath, "I have one thousand coins around my waist. They are very heavy, so I have fallen behind."

His companion said with anxiety, "Just throw away the coins right now if you want to survive."

The person gave no answer, just shaking his head. After a short while, he became even more tired from swimming.

The companions who had come ashore shouted to him, "You're so stupid! You are going to drown. What can you do with the money then?"

做贼心虚・沈括《梦溪笔谈》

A Thief Has Guilty Conscience © *Mengxi Bitan* by Shen Kuo

A Thief Has Guilty Conscience

◎ *Mengxi Bitan* by Shen Kuo

Chen Shugu, an academician of the Privy Council, once acted as the magistrate of Pucheng County in Fujian Province. A few suspects were caught after somebody lost something. To identify the true criminal, Chen Shugu tricked them by saying, "A bell in a temple can tell the true robber without fail."

Chen then ordered his men to get the bell, put it in the backyard, took the suspects to stand before the bell, and announced, "If a person has not stolen, then the bell will not ring when he touches it; and if a person has stolen, then the bell will ring when he touches it."

With serious expressions, Chen Shugu and his colleagues prayed and sacrificed in front of the bell. After the sacrifice, the bell was wrapped with a curtain, and someone was ordered to spread ink on the bell.

After a short while, Chen Shugu ordered the suspects to enter the curtain and touch the bell. When they came out, Chen Shugu inspected their hands, finding the hands of only one person had no ink. Then, Chen Shugu tried the person, who confessed his crime.

The person, a thief with a guilty conscience, was afraid the bell would ring if he touched it, and thus didn't touch the bell.

Nowhere to Exert Power

◎ *A Collection of Su Dongpo*

by Su Shi

There lived a large number of tigers in Zhong County, Wan County and Yunyang County of Sichuan Province in the ancient time.

One day, a woman was doing some washing while her two children played on the beach.

A spotted tiger suddenly ran down from the mountain, and the woman jumped into the water in a hurry to avoid the tiger. However, the children still played on the beach, and were not afraid at all. Finding this strange, the

tiger ran toward the children, stared at them for a long time, and even bumped them with his head, hoping the children would fear him. However, the children were not afraid at all and patted the head of the tiger and held its ears. The tiger smiled and finally left.

Before eating a human, the tiger will surely exert its power first, but this won't work in face of the human who doesn't fear him.

州官放火 · 陆游《老学庵笔记》

A Bossy Official © *Notes in the Old Study* by Lu You

A Bossy Official

◎ *Notes in the Old Study*

by Lu You

After Tian Deng became the magistrate of a shire, he resented being called by his name, and would get irritated when others offended him by calling by name. Many of his officials were beaten up because of this. To avoid the wrath of their magistrate, the people in the shire referred to "lights (pronounced "deng" in Chinese)" as "fire".

When the Lantern Festival came, the authority specifically allowed the public to view the lanterns (pronounced "denglong" in Chinese) in the capital of the shire, and posted a notice on the street that read, "This shire will display fire for three days."

得过且过 · 陶宗仪《南村辍耕录》

Drift Along © *Nancun Chuogenglu* by Tao Zongyi

Drift Along

◎ *Nancun Chuogenglu* by Tao Zongyi

It was said that a bird called the winter-wailing bird lived in Mount Wutai.

The bird had very beautiful, colorful feathers every hot summer. What he did all day long was to sing once and again, "Aha! The phoenix is inferior to me! The phoenix is inferior to me!" Other birds were busy making nests, but he kept singing without stopping.

When autumn came, it started to become cool, but he was still boasting his beautiful feathers, while other birds were building homes on a tight schedule. Other birds advised him, "Winter is coming. You better make a nest now otherwise you will freeze to death if it snows."

The bird answered, "It does not matter, take it easy, and I will do it tomorrow." He said "tomorrow" today, and also said "tomorrow" the day after tomorrow.

Soon winter came, but he had not built his nest yet. His beautiful feathers fell off gradually, and he became naked in the cold winter. When the cold winter came, he was trembling from the frost and could not sing clearly to change "the phoenix is inferior to me" to "drift along".

One day, a severe wind came, and it snowed a heavy snow. The winter-wailing bird died the next day.

A Greedy Heart ◎ *Longmenzi Ningdaoji* by Song Lian

A Greedy Heart

◎ *Longmenzi Ningdaoji*

by Song Lian

A person in the State Jin was very greedy. One day, he saw various types of goods at the marketplace, and took them while thinking aloud, "I may cook a dish with this meat, make clothes with this cloth, and carry things with this bag." The person turned around to run away with a lot of things in his hand.

The marketplace administrator asked him, "Why do you rob others of their properties even in public?"

The person answered, "When my greedy

heart is very strong, I will think all the things in the world should belong to me, and don't know at all they belong to others. If I take the things of a person, it will be his good luck. When I become rich, I will reward him by folds."

Seeing the person was so stubborn and reluctant to correct his mistake, the marketplace administrator whipped him, and took back these things. When driven by greed, a person will just take the belongings of others even in public. Once a person loses his wit because of greed, he will do many unimaginable things.

兄弟争雁 · 刘元卿《贤奕编》

Brothers Fight for a Wild Goose © *Xianyi Bian* by Liu Yuanqing

Brothers Fight for a Wild Goose

◎ *Xianyi Bian* by Liu Yuanqing

Once upon a time, a person saw a wild goose fly in the sky, and prepared to shoot it down with an arrow. He said, "I will boil the wild goose after shooting it down." His brother disagreed him, "It's suitable to boil the wild goose, but it's best to roast it." Both brothers kept arguing and refused to yield to each other, so they went to She Bo for arbitration. She Bo provided them with a compromise: Cut the wild goose in two halves, and one half was boiled, and the other half was roasted. The brothers thought this was a good idea. However, when they returned to look for the wild goose, it had disappeared.

万字 · 刘元卿《贤弈编》

The Word of Wan ◎ *Xianyi Bian* by Liu Yuanqing

The Word of Wan

◎ *Xianyi Bian* by Liu Yuanqing

There was a very rich farmer in Ruzhou who had several generations of illiterates in his family. One year, the farmer retained a teacher from the Chu area to teach his son. The teacher first taught his son to imitate the master sheet, and told him after one stroke, "This is the word of one (一)", taught the son after two strokes, "This is the word of two (二)", and said after three strokes, "This is the word of three (三)."

Before the teacher finished his remarks, the child happily threw away his calligraphy

writing brush, and went to tell his father, "I have learned the rule, and no longer need the teacher. Please dismiss him as soon as possible so as to not waste money."

Seeing that his son had learned so quickly, the father was overjoyed, and dismissed the teacher after paying for the tuition.

Shortly after that, the father wanted to invite a friend surnamed Wan (both mean ten thousand and a surname in Chinese "万") to a dinner, and so asked his son to write the letter of invitation. However, the son didn't finish the letter after a long period of time. The father became very impatient, and came to rush his son.

The son said angrily, "There are so many surnames in the world. Why is Wan the surname of your friend? I have just written five hundred strokes from morning until now."

A scholar with very limited knowledge would think he had learned everything if he understood something by accident just like the person who wrote the word of Wan.

劳山道士・蒲松龄《聊斋志异》

The Taoist of Lao Mountain © *Strange Tales of a Lonely Studio* by Pu Songling

The Taoist of Lao Mountain

◎ *Strange Tales of a Lonely Studio*

by Pu Songling

Once there was a young man called Wang Sheng who lived in the county. He was the seventh child in a rich family, and liked Taoism since he was a small child. Learning there were many immortals in Lao Mountain, he carried his luggage to look for immortals.

Wang Sheng arrived at a quiet Taoist temple, and saw a Taoist sitting on a patch of grass. With silver hair reaching his shoulders and an unworldly manner, the Taoist seemed like a true immortal. Wang Sheng hurried to kneel down and they had a talk. The Taoist

was very eloquent and witty. Wang Sheng admired the Taoist very much, and wanted to learn from him. The Taoist said, "I am afraid you are spoiled and lazy, and are unable to tolerate hardship." Wang Sheng immediately answered, "No problem, I can endure any hardship." The Taoist had many students, and Wang Sheng met them in the dark when the disciples went together. Then, he stayed in the Taoist temple as a Taoist student.

Next morning, the Taoist called Wang Sheng, gave him an ax and asked him to chop wood in the mountain along with other disciples. Wang Sheng accepted the order. More than one month passed, Wang Sheng endured various hardships, his once delicate skin gradually became very coarse, and his hands and feet had thick calluses. He could no longer endure the hardship of chopping wood every day, and had the thought of going home.

More than a month passed but the Taoist had not taught him a single skill. Wang Sheng could no long tolerate it, and said goodbye to

the Taoist, "I have come here from a distant place to learn Taoist skills from you. Even if I can't learn the theurgy of being immortal, I still want you to teach me the small skills to satisfy my thirst for theurgy. Now, I have been here for a month only chopping wood every day from dawn until dusk. When I was at home I had never suffered so many hardships." Hearing what Wang Sheng had said, the Taoist laughed aloud, "I told you that you could not tolerate hardship, and this proved to be true. I will let you go home tomorrow morning." Wang Sheng requested, "I have been here working for a period of time, so I want you to teach me a small skill so that my trip will be worthwhile." The Taoist asked, "What do you want to learn?" Wang Sheng replied, "Each time I see you walk, even the wall will not stop you. If I can learn this skill, I will be satisfied." The Taoist laughed and agreed to teach Wang Sheng the secret. Taking Wang Sheng to a wall, the Taoist asked Wang Sheng to read the incantation, and

cried, “Enter!” However, when coming in front of the wall, Wang Sheng didn’t dare to walk ahead. The Taoist cried again, “Try to enter!” Calming himself down, Wang Sheng was poised to step forward, but stopped by the wall. The Taoist instructed, “Lower your head and rush into it without hesitation.” Wang Sheng went several steps back and rushed towards the wall. He felt as if he had touched the wall, but the wall was empty and didn’t prevent him from moving forward. Looking back, he found himself already standing on the other side of the wall. Wang Sheng was overjoyed, and thanked the Taoist. The Taoist said, “You need to have a noble mind after you return home, or otherwise the theurgy will not work.” Then, the Taoist gave Wang Sheng some money as the travel expense, and let him go home.

After returning home, Wang Sheng told everybody he had met an immortal and learned the very powerful theurgy. He boasted that he could penetrate a wall, no matter how

solid it was. His wife didn't believe him at all, and Wang Sheng decided to display the theurgy to her. As instructed by the Taoist, he rushed to the wall from several meters away from the wall. However, his head hit the wall and he fell to the ground. He stood up with the help of his wife, and a lump like an egg appeared on his forehead. His wife laughed at his gullibleness at trusting others while consoling him at the same time. Wang Sheng was very angry and blamed the Taoist for ill intentions.

点石成金・石成金《笑得好》

The Midas Touch ◎ *A Collection of Jokes* by Shi Chengjin

The Midas Touch

◎ A Collection of Jokes
by Shi Chengjin

An immortal came to the human world to test the human nature of the Midas touch. He selected a less greedy person, and provide him an opportunity to become an immortal. However, to his disappointment, every person he had met was so greedy that they were dissatisfied, even though he had changed a huge stone into gold. He was really disappointed, and said, "People are no longer simple and greediness is limitless!"

Later, the immortal came across a person. The immortal pointed at a huge stone

before him, and said, "I will change this stone into gold for you." The person shook his head in refusal. Thinking that the person probably thought the stone was small, the immortal pointed at a larger stone, "I will change this extremely huge stone into gold for you." The person still shook his head in refusal.

The immortal found the person not greedy at all, and gave him an opportunity to become an immortal. He then asked the person, "You want neither the big gold nor the small gold. What on earth do you want?" The person stretched his finger and said, "I want nothing, but just your finger that changes stones into gold. I want to tie it to my own finger so that I will own limitless amounts of gold wherever I go."

The Ambition of the Wolves

◎ *Fantastic Tales* by Ji Yun

By chance, a rich person caught two baby wolves. He took them home and raised them together with his dogs. The baby wolves and dogs got along well, and often happily played with each other. The baby wolves gradually grew up, but were very tamed and continued to get along well with the dogs. The person forgot that they were wolves.

One day, the person took a catnap in the sitting room. He awoke to dogs wildly barking. He found nobody around him. He fell back to sleep, but the dogs barked again. Having an odd feeling about the barking, he did not rise, but instead pretended to be asleep, with his eyes slightly open to observe what was happening. He found that the two wolves wanted to bite his throat when he was asleep just now, but the dogs barked wildly in order to stop the wolves. The person was very angry, and killed the wolves, and removed their coats.